What a surpri

Two surprises

"What are you reading, Ben?" asked Mum.

Ben said, "It's my reading book from school. It's good."

"Will you read some of it to me?"
asked Mum.

"Yes," said Ben. "I like this.
Run, run,
As fast as you can.
You can't catch me.
I'm the Gingerbread Man."

Dad said, "That was good.
Read some for me now."

"I can't," said Ben.
"That's the end of the book."

"And I want to go shopping," said Mum.

"Can we come?" said Liz and Ben.

"Yes. We'll all go," said Mum.

"Come on, children."

As they went to the shops, Ben said,
"The Gingerbread Man said,
You can't catch me,
but the fox got him.
Do you think the fox liked
eating the Gingerbread Man?"

"Oh, yes," said Liz.
"**We** like eating gingerbread men."

Mum and Dad laughed.

"Let's go to the supermarket," said Mum.
"We can get all the shopping here."

The children helped Mum and Dad
do the shopping.
They soon got it all.
"Come on, Mum," said Dad.
"We want to go home for tea."

Mum had a bag.

"What's in that bag?" asked Dad.

"It's a surprise," said Mum.

"Is it something for tea?" asked Liz.

"Wait and see," said Mum.

They came out of the supermarket.

"Wait here," said Dad.

"I want to get something."

"Be quick," said Mum.

"We want to get home for tea."

Dad went into a little shop.

Dad came back with a bag.

"What's that?" asked Ben.

"Is it something to eat?" asked Liz.

"Wait and see.
It's a surprise," said Dad.

They got home.

"Can we have the surprises now?"
asked the children.

"Wait," said Mum.
"Help Dad put the shopping away, and
I'll get the tea."

So the children helped Dad, and
Mum got the tea.

"Now," said Mum.

"Here is my surprise."

"Gingerbread men!" said Ben.

"What's your surprise, Dad?"
asked Liz.

"Gingerbread men!" they all shouted.

"What a surprise!" said Ben.

"Two gingerbread men each," said Liz.

Mum's surprise

Liz, Ben, and Dad
were out in the garden.
Mum was at the shops.

Ben said, "What can we do now?"

"Can we make a cake, Dad?" asked Liz.
"It will be a surprise for Mum."

"Yes," said Dad.
"Let's make a cake for tea."

"Let's see what we want," said Dad.
"You get me two eggs, Liz.
Ben, get the milk."

The children went to get
the eggs and the milk.

"Here are two eggs," said Liz.

"I can't find the milk," said Ben.

"Where is it, then?" asked Dad.

Liz said, "It's out here.
You take one in, Ben.
I can take two."

"Ben, you put the eggs in," said Dad.
"Liz, put in the milk.
Now let's mix it up."

"It can go in the oven now."
Dad put the cake in the oven.

"Help me put the things away," said Dad.

The children helped Dad.

"Good," said Dad. "Now we can go
into the garden."

"Can we take the cake out now?"
asked Ben.

"Wait," said Dad.
"We can take it out soon."

"Can't we just look at it?" said Liz.

"No," said Dad. "Wait!"

The children played and
Dad went to sleep.

"Here's Mum," said Ben.

"The cake!" shouted Dad.

"The cake!" shouted Ben.

"Quick!" shouted Liz.

They all ran in.

"What's that?" asked Mum.

"It was a cake," said Dad.

"We wanted to make
you a surprise," said Liz.

"What a surprise!" said Mum.

"I have a surprise for you," said Mum.

"Have you got some
gingerbread men?" asked Liz.
Mum got a big cake out
of her shopping bag.
They all laughed and had tea.